"I CAN NEVER DECIDE WHETHER MY DREAMS ARE THE RESULT OF MY THOUGHTS, OR MY THOUGHTS THE RESULT OF MY DREAMS."

—D. H. LAWRENCE

DREAM JOURNAL

KNOCK KNOCK®
VENICE, CALIFORNIA

Created and published by Knock Knock
Distributed by Who's There Inc.
Venice, CA 90291
knockknockstuff.com

Made in China

ISBN: 978-160106523-0
UPC: 825703-50062-2

10 9 8 7 6 5 4

DREAMING 101

Humans have produced rich traditions of dream interpretation since the dawn of history. While contemporary thinking privileges a physiological or psychoanalytic explanation of dreaming, earlier cultures explored dreams as divine messages, prophesies, instructions for healing, alternate worlds, and extensions of reality. Though our sleeping habits have changed—we now sleep differently and less—we can learn a thing or two from the way our ancestors thought about and interpreted dreaming.

Indigenous cultures have enhanced their dreams with fasting, traveling, hallucinogens, and—ironically—sleep deprivation. Some Native Americans imagined that dreams flew around at night and could be caught with a dream catcher net. In tribal societies, dreams often comprised an alternative spiritual reality to which humans gained access only through the dream state.

Developments in dream reflection, understanding, and analysis have occurred over the centuries, and have been tackled by every culture from the ancient Egyptians to contemporary psychologists in Western culture like Sigmund Freud and Carl Jung. The Romans believed dreams were so important that Emperor Augustus proclaimed that anyone who dreamed of Rome must relate the dream publicly in case it contained a prophecy about Rome's well-being. It's clear that the significance of our dreams has been a preoccupation throughout the history of human life.

Contemporary thinkers came at dreams with a fresh analytical perspective and it was evident that change was in the air when Sigmund Freud penned his classic *The Interpretation of Dreams* in 1900. Dreams contributed significantly to Freud's emerging exploration of psychoanalysis, a discipline of examination into the self with new ways to explore subjectivity. He sought to apply modern scientific principles to dream interpretation, analyzing not only his patient's dreams but also his own, in order to develop a clinically applicable method for understanding the mind. In Freud's view, dreams provided data. Correctly decoded, dreams could yield insight into underlying conflict.

With dream recording and interpretation, there are a few important steps to follow to find what you're looking for. Writing down your dreams immediately upon waking, sketching the most immediate and vivid detail, and attempting interpretation no matter your skill set are all steps one can take to further understanding in a murky world. The helpful tips that follow show you how to make the most of the perplexing time we spend in sleep and the visual manifestation of our deepest emotions, feelings, and fears. Dream on.

HELPFUL TIPS

BEFORE SLEEP

01. Keep this Dream Journal and a pen or pencil beside your bed.

02. Try to maintain a regular sleep schedule, going to bed and waking up at approximately the same times each day.

03. Avoid alcohol, sleeping pills, and other drugs before bed; they can interfere with normal sleep cycles and dreaming.

04. When you lie down to sleep, take a moment to empty your head of daily concerns and actually tell yourself to remember your dreams.

05. Waking up without an alarm clock is optimal for natural dream recall.

AFTER WAKING

06. While still in bed, pick up your Dream Journal and start recording. At this point, you are merely transcribing the dream, not interpreting.

07. Write down brief descriptions of images, people, animals, places, impressions—anything you remember from the dream. Pay special attention to emotions you felt during the dream.

08. Log your dreams as freely as possible! Don't concern yourself with writing quality or whether the dream makes sense. Simply transcribe.

DREAM ANALYSIS

09. Unlike recording, there is no urgency to reflecting on your dream. In fact, returning to it at a later date could free up emotional space to process the dream.

10. Look for recurring images in your dream(s). These could be anything from people to animals to locations to numbers, even colors.

11. Examine quality of movement and action in dreams, such as ascending or descending staircases, flying, driving, swimming, running toward or away from something, or falling.

12. Think about your own role in the dream. Did you act differently or the same as you'd normally act in waking life?

13. The same question applies to the other characters in the dream. Were they people you know? Did they act according to your expectations? Were there people you didn't recognize? Could they represent someone in your life, or are they similar to you in any way?

14. Compare dream images to events or concerns in your waking life.

15. Read through your Dream Journal every so often with an eye for themes, patterns, repetition, and change. Over time this record of your inner world will yield meaning, creativity, and insight, and perhaps a funny story or two.

ZZZ

RECORD
WHAT HAPPENED?

TITLE:

DATE:

☐ Nightmare ☐ Fantasy ☐ Symbolic ☐ Mundane ☐ Just plain bizarre

WHAT WAS THE PREVAILING EMOTION?

☐ Fear ☐ Frustration ☐ Loss of self ☐ Arousal
☐ Humiliation ☐ Grief ☐ Love ☐ Anger
☐ Freedom ☐ Paralysis ☐ Confusion ☐ Panic
☐ Joy ☐ Surprise ☐ Vulnerability ☐ ____________

HAVE YOU DREAMED THIS DREAM BEFORE?

☐ Yes ☐ No ☐ Maybe so ☐ I wish ☐ Once was enough, thanks

SKETCH

HOW WOULD YOU DRAW IT?

☐ Frame-worthy ☐ An accurate rendering ☐ Close enough ☐ Crap

REFLECT

WHAT'S YOUR INTERPRETATION?

☐ Significant ☐ Insignificant ☐ Reexamine later ☐ Dream understood

RECORD
WHAT HAPPENED?

TITLE:

DATE:

☐ Nightmare ☐ Fantasy ☐ Symbolic ☐ Mundane ☐ Just plain bizarre

WHAT WAS THE PREVAILING EMOTION?

☐ Fear ☐ Frustration ☐ Loss of self ☐ Arousal
☐ Humiliation ☐ Grief ☐ Love ☐ Anger
☐ Freedom ☐ Paralysis ☐ Confusion ☐ Panic
☐ Joy ☐ Surprise ☐ Vulnerability ☐ ________

HAVE YOU DREAMED THIS DREAM BEFORE?

☐ Yes ☐ No ☐ Maybe so ☐ I wish ☐ Once was enough, thanks

SKETCH

HOW WOULD YOU DRAW IT?

☐ Frame-worthy ☐ An accurate rendering ☐ Close enough ☐ Crap

REFLECT

WHAT'S YOUR INTERPRETATION?

☐ Significant ☐ Insignificant ☐ Reexamine later ☐ Dream understood

RECORD
WHAT HAPPENED?

TITLE:

DATE:

☐ Nightmare ☐ Fantasy ☐ Symbolic ☐ Mundane ☐ Just plain bizarre

WHAT WAS THE PREVAILING EMOTION?

☐ Fear ☐ Frustration ☐ Loss of self ☐ Arousal
☐ Humiliation ☐ Grief ☐ Love ☐ Anger
☐ Freedom ☐ Paralysis ☐ Confusion ☐ Panic
☐ Joy ☐ Surprise ☐ Vulnerability ☐ ____________

HAVE YOU DREAMED THIS DREAM BEFORE?

☐ Yes ☐ No ☐ Maybe so ☐ I wish ☐ Once was enough, thanks

SKETCH
HOW WOULD YOU DRAW IT?

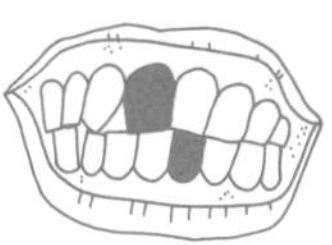

☐ Frame-worthy ☐ An accurate rendering ☐ Close enough ☐ Crap

REFLECT
WHAT'S YOUR INTERPRETATION?

☐ Significant ☐ Insignificant ☐ Reexamine later ☐ Dream understood

RECORD

WHAT HAPPENED?

TITLE:

DATE:

☐ Nightmare ☐ Fantasy ☐ Symbolic ☐ Mundane ☐ Just plain bizarre

WHAT WAS THE PREVAILING EMOTION?

☐ Fear ☐ Frustration ☐ Loss of self ☐ Arousal
☐ Humiliation ☐ Grief ☐ Love ☐ Anger
☐ Freedom ☐ Paralysis ☐ Confusion ☐ Panic
☐ Joy ☐ Surprise ☐ Vulnerability ☐ ____________

HAVE YOU DREAMED THIS DREAM BEFORE?

☐ Yes ☐ No ☐ Maybe so ☐ I wish ☐ Once was enough, thanks

SKETCH

HOW WOULD YOU DRAW IT?

☐ Frame-worthy ☐ An accurate rendering ☐ Close enough ☐ Crap

REFLECT

WHAT'S YOUR INTERPRETATION?

☐ Significant ☐ Insignificant ☐ Reexamine later ☐ Dream understood

RECORD
WHAT HAPPENED?

TITLE:
DATE:

☐ Nightmare ☐ Fantasy ☐ Symbolic ☐ Mundane ☐ Just plain bizarre

WHAT WAS THE PREVAILING EMOTION?

☐ Fear ☐ Frustration ☐ Loss of self ☐ Arousal
☐ Humiliation ☐ Grief ☐ Love ☐ Anger
☐ Freedom ☐ Paralysis ☐ Confusion ☐ Panic
☐ Joy ☐ Surprise ☐ Vulnerability ☐ ___________

HAVE YOU DREAMED THIS DREAM BEFORE?

☐ Yes ☐ No ☐ Maybe so ☐ I wish ☐ Once was enough, thanks

SKETCH

HOW WOULD YOU DRAW IT?

☐ Frame-worthy ☐ An accurate rendering ☐ Close enough ☐ Crap

REFLECT

WHAT'S YOUR INTERPRETATION?

☐ Significant ☐ Insignificant ☐ Reexamine later ☐ Dream understood

RECORD
WHAT HAPPENED?

TITLE:

DATE:

☐ Nightmare ☐ Fantasy ☐ Symbolic ☐ Mundane ☐ Just plain bizarre

WHAT WAS THE PREVAILING EMOTION?

☐ Fear ☐ Frustration ☐ Loss of self ☐ Arousal
☐ Humiliation ☐ Grief ☐ Love ☐ Anger
☐ Freedom ☐ Paralysis ☐ Confusion ☐ Panic
☐ Joy ☐ Surprise ☐ Vulnerability ☐ ____________

HAVE YOU DREAMED THIS DREAM BEFORE?

☐ Yes ☐ No ☐ Maybe so ☐ I wish ☐ Once was enough, thanks

SKETCH

HOW WOULD YOU DRAW IT?

☐ Frame-worthy ☐ An accurate rendering ☐ Close enough ☐ Crap

REFLECT

WHAT'S YOUR INTERPRETATION?

☐ Significant ☐ Insignificant ☐ Reexamine later ☐ Dream understood

RECORD
WHAT HAPPENED?

TITLE:
DATE:

☐ Nightmare ☐ Fantasy ☐ Symbolic ☐ Mundane ☐ Just plain bizarre

WHAT WAS THE PREVAILING EMOTION?

☐ Fear	☐ Frustration	☐ Loss of self	☐ Arousal
☐ Humiliation	☐ Grief	☐ Love	☐ Anger
☐ Freedom	☐ Paralysis	☐ Confusion	☐ Panic
☐ Joy	☐ Surprise	☐ Vulnerability	☐ ______

HAVE YOU DREAMED THIS DREAM BEFORE?

☐ Yes ☐ No ☐ Maybe so ☐ I wish ☐ Once was enough, thanks

SKETCH
HOW WOULD YOU DRAW IT?

☐ Frame-worthy ☐ An accurate rendering ☐ Close enough ☐ Crap

REFLECT
WHAT'S YOUR INTERPRETATION?

☐ Significant ☐ Insignificant ☐ Reexamine later ☐ Dream understood

RECORD

WHAT HAPPENED?

TITLE:

DATE:

☐ Nightmare ☐ Fantasy ☐ Symbolic ☐ Mundane ☐ Just plain bizarre

WHAT WAS THE PREVAILING EMOTION?

☐ Fear
☐ Humiliation
☐ Freedom
☐ Joy
☐ Frustration
☐ Grief
☐ Paralysis
☐ Surprise
☐ Loss of self
☐ Love
☐ Confusion
☐ Vulnerability
☐ Arousal
☐ Anger
☐ Panic
☐ ____________

HAVE YOU DREAMED THIS DREAM BEFORE?

☐ Yes ☐ No ☐ Maybe so ☐ I wish ☐ Once was enough, thanks

SKETCH

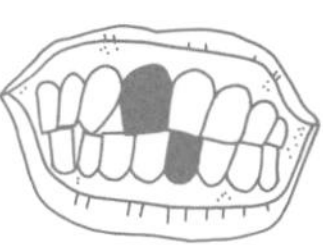

HOW WOULD YOU DRAW IT?

☐ Frame-worthy ☐ An accurate rendering ☐ Close enough ☐ Crap

REFLECT

WHAT'S YOUR INTERPRETATION?

☐ Significant ☐ Insignificant ☐ Reexamine later ☐ Dream understood

RECORD

WHAT HAPPENED?

TITLE:

DATE:

☐ Nightmare ☐ Fantasy ☐ Symbolic ☐ Mundane ☐ Just plain bizarre

WHAT WAS THE PREVAILING EMOTION?

☐ Fear ☐ Frustration ☐ Loss of self ☐ Arousal
☐ Humiliation ☐ Grief ☐ Love ☐ Anger
☐ Freedom ☐ Paralysis ☐ Confusion ☐ Panic
☐ Joy ☐ Surprise ☐ Vulnerability ☐ ________

HAVE YOU DREAMED THIS DREAM BEFORE?

☐ Yes ☐ No ☐ Maybe so ☐ I wish ☐ Once was enough, thanks

SKETCH

HOW WOULD YOU DRAW IT?

☐ Frame-worthy ☐ An accurate rendering ☐ Close enough ☐ Crap

REFLECT

WHAT'S YOUR INTERPRETATION?

☐ Significant ☐ Insignificant ☐ Reexamine later ☐ Dream understood

RECORD
WHAT HAPPENED?

TITLE:

DATE:

☐ Nightmare ☐ Fantasy ☐ Symbolic ☐ Mundane ☐ Just plain bizarre

WHAT WAS THE PREVAILING EMOTION?

☐ Fear ☐ Frustration ☐ Loss of self ☐ Arousal
☐ Humiliation ☐ Grief ☐ Love ☐ Anger
☐ Freedom ☐ Paralysis ☐ Confusion ☐ Panic
☐ Joy ☐ Surprise ☐ Vulnerability ☐ ____________

HAVE YOU DREAMED THIS DREAM BEFORE?

☐ Yes ☐ No ☐ Maybe so ☐ I wish ☐ Once was enough, thanks

SKETCH

HOW WOULD YOU DRAW IT?

☐ Frame-worthy ☐ An accurate rendering ☐ Close enough ☐ Crap

REFLECT

WHAT'S YOUR INTERPRETATION?

☐ Significant ☐ Insignificant ☐ Reexamine later ☐ Dream understood

RECORD
WHAT HAPPENED?

TITLE:

DATE:

☐ Nightmare ☐ Fantasy ☐ Symbolic ☐ Mundane ☐ Just plain bizarre

WHAT WAS THE PREVAILING EMOTION?

☐ Fear ☐ Frustration ☐ Loss of self ☐ Arousal
☐ Humiliation ☐ Grief ☐ Love ☐ Anger
☐ Freedom ☐ Paralysis ☐ Confusion ☐ Panic
☐ Joy ☐ Surprise ☐ Vulnerability ☐ ______________

HAVE YOU DREAMED THIS DREAM BEFORE?

☐ Yes ☐ No ☐ Maybe so ☐ I wish ☐ Once was enough, thanks

SKETCH

HOW WOULD YOU DRAW IT?

☐ Frame-worthy ☐ An accurate rendering ☐ Close enough ☐ Crap

REFLECT

WHAT'S YOUR INTERPRETATION?

☐ Significant ☐ Insignificant ☐ Reexamine later ☐ Dream understood

RECORD
WHAT HAPPENED?

TITLE:
DATE:

☐ Nightmare ☐ Fantasy ☐ Symbolic ☐ Mundane ☐ Just plain bizarre

WHAT WAS THE PREVAILING EMOTION?

☐ Fear	☐ Frustration	☐ Loss of self	☐ Arousal
☐ Humiliation	☐ Grief	☐ Love	☐ Anger
☐ Freedom	☐ Paralysis	☐ Confusion	☐ Panic
☐ Joy	☐ Surprise	☐ Vulnerability	☐ ______

HAVE YOU DREAMED THIS DREAM BEFORE?

☐ Yes ☐ No ☐ Maybe so ☐ I wish ☐ Once was enough, thanks

SKETCH
HOW WOULD YOU DRAW IT?

☐ Frame-worthy ☐ An accurate rendering ☐ Close enough ☐ Crap

REFLECT
WHAT'S YOUR INTERPRETATION?

☐ Significant ☐ Insignificant ☐ Reexamine later ☐ Dream understood

RECORD
WHAT HAPPENED?

TITLE:

DATE:

☐ Nightmare ☐ Fantasy ☐ Symbolic ☐ Mundane ☐ Just plain bizarre

WHAT WAS THE PREVAILING EMOTION?

☐ Fear ☐ Frustration ☐ Loss of self ☐ Arousal
☐ Humiliation ☐ Grief ☐ Love ☐ Anger
☐ Freedom ☐ Paralysis ☐ Confusion ☐ Panic
☐ Joy ☐ Surprise ☐ Vulnerability ☐ ________

HAVE YOU DREAMED THIS DREAM BEFORE?

☐ Yes ☐ No ☐ Maybe so ☐ I wish ☐ Once was enough, thanks

SKETCH

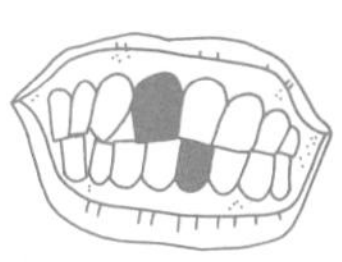

HOW WOULD YOU DRAW IT?

☐ Frame-worthy ☐ An accurate rendering ☐ Close enough ☐ Crap

REFLECT

WHAT'S YOUR INTERPRETATION?

☐ Significant ☐ Insignificant ☐ Reexamine later ☐ Dream understood

RECORD
WHAT HAPPENED?

TITLE:
DATE:

☐ Nightmare ☐ Fantasy ☐ Symbolic ☐ Mundane ☐ Just plain bizarre

WHAT WAS THE PREVAILING EMOTION?

☐ Fear ☐ Frustration ☐ Loss of self ☐ Arousal
☐ Humiliation ☐ Grief ☐ Love ☐ Anger
☐ Freedom ☐ Paralysis ☐ Confusion ☐ Panic
☐ Joy ☐ Surprise ☐ Vulnerability ☐ ____________

HAVE YOU DREAMED THIS DREAM BEFORE?

☐ Yes ☐ No ☐ Maybe so ☐ I wish ☐ Once was enough, thanks

SKETCH
HOW WOULD YOU DRAW IT?

☐ Frame-worthy ☐ An accurate rendering ☐ Close enough ☐ Crap

REFLECT
WHAT'S YOUR INTERPRETATION?

☐ Significant ☐ Insignificant ☐ Reexamine later ☐ Dream understood

RECORD
WHAT HAPPENED?

TITLE:
DATE:

☐ Nightmare ☐ Fantasy ☐ Symbolic ☐ Mundane ☐ Just plain bizarre

WHAT WAS THE PREVAILING EMOTION?

☐ Fear ☐ Frustration ☐ Loss of self ☐ Arousal
☐ Humiliation ☐ Grief ☐ Love ☐ Anger
☐ Freedom ☐ Paralysis ☐ Confusion ☐ Panic
☐ Joy ☐ Surprise ☐ Vulnerability ☐ ____________

HAVE YOU DREAMED THIS DREAM BEFORE?

☐ Yes ☐ No ☐ Maybe so ☐ I wish ☐ Once was enough, thanks

SKETCH

HOW WOULD YOU DRAW IT?

☐ Frame-worthy ☐ An accurate rendering ☐ Close enough ☐ Crap

REFLECT

WHAT'S YOUR INTERPRETATION?

☐ Significant ☐ Insignificant ☐ Reexamine later ☐ Dream understood

RECORD

WHAT HAPPENED?

TITLE:

DATE:

☐ Nightmare ☐ Fantasy ☐ Symbolic ☐ Mundane ☐ Just plain bizarre

WHAT WAS THE PREVAILING EMOTION?

☐ Fear ☐ Frustration ☐ Loss of self ☐ Arousal
☐ Humiliation ☐ Grief ☐ Love ☐ Anger
☐ Freedom ☐ Paralysis ☐ Confusion ☐ Panic
☐ Joy ☐ Surprise ☐ Vulnerability ☐ ________

HAVE YOU DREAMED THIS DREAM BEFORE?

☐ Yes ☐ No ☐ Maybe so ☐ I wish ☐ Once was enough, thanks

SKETCH

HOW WOULD YOU DRAW IT?

☐ Frame-worthy ☐ An accurate rendering ☐ Close enough ☐ Crap

REFLECT

WHAT'S YOUR INTERPRETATION?

☐ Significant ☐ Insignificant ☐ Reexamine later ☐ Dream understood

RECORD
WHAT HAPPENED?

TITLE:

DATE:

☐ Nightmare ☐ Fantasy ☐ Symbolic ☐ Mundane ☐ Just plain bizarre

WHAT WAS THE PREVAILING EMOTION?

☐ Fear ☐ Frustration ☐ Loss of self ☐ Arousal
☐ Humiliation ☐ Grief ☐ Love ☐ Anger
☐ Freedom ☐ Paralysis ☐ Confusion ☐ Panic
☐ Joy ☐ Surprise ☐ Vulnerability ☐ ______

HAVE YOU DREAMED THIS DREAM BEFORE?

☐ Yes ☐ No ☐ Maybe so ☐ I wish ☐ Once was enough, thanks

SKETCH

HOW WOULD YOU DRAW IT?

☐ Frame-worthy ☐ An accurate rendering ☐ Close enough ☐ Crap

REFLECT

WHAT'S YOUR INTERPRETATION?

☐ Significant ☐ Insignificant ☐ Reexamine later ☐ Dream understood

RECORD
WHAT HAPPENED?

TITLE:

DATE:

☐ Nightmare ☐ Fantasy ☐ Symbolic ☐ Mundane ☐ Just plain bizarre

WHAT WAS THE PREVAILING EMOTION?

☐ Fear	☐ Frustration	☐ Loss of self	☐ Arousal
☐ Humiliation	☐ Grief	☐ Love	☐ Anger
☐ Freedom	☐ Paralysis	☐ Confusion	☐ Panic
☐ Joy	☐ Surprise	☐ Vulnerability	☐ ________

HAVE YOU DREAMED THIS DREAM BEFORE?

☐ Yes ☐ No ☐ Maybe so ☐ I wish ☐ Once was enough, thanks

SKETCH

HOW WOULD YOU DRAW IT?

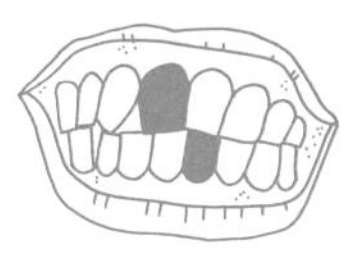

☐ Frame-worthy ☐ An accurate rendering ☐ Close enough ☐ Crap

REFLECT

WHAT'S YOUR INTERPRETATION?

☐ Significant ☐ Insignificant ☐ Reexamine later ☐ Dream understood

RECORD
WHAT HAPPENED?

TITLE:

DATE:

☐ Nightmare ☐ Fantasy ☐ Symbolic ☐ Mundane ☐ Just plain bizarre

WHAT WAS THE PREVAILING EMOTION?

☐ Fear ☐ Frustration ☐ Loss of self ☐ Arousal
☐ Humiliation ☐ Grief ☐ Love ☐ Anger
☐ Freedom ☐ Paralysis ☐ Confusion ☐ Panic
☐ Joy ☐ Surprise ☐ Vulnerability ☐ ________

HAVE YOU DREAMED THIS DREAM BEFORE?

☐ Yes ☐ No ☐ Maybe so ☐ I wish ☐ Once was enough, thanks

SKETCH
HOW WOULD YOU DRAW IT?

☐ Frame-worthy ☐ An accurate rendering ☐ Close enough ☐ Crap

REFLECT
WHAT'S YOUR INTERPRETATION?

☐ Significant ☐ Insignificant ☐ Reexamine later ☐ Dream understood

RECORD
WHAT HAPPENED?

TITLE:

DATE:

☐ Nightmare ☐ Fantasy ☐ Symbolic ☐ Mundane ☐ Just plain bizarre

WHAT WAS THE PREVAILING EMOTION?

☐ Fear ☐ Frustration ☐ Loss of self ☐ Arousal
☐ Humiliation ☐ Grief ☐ Love ☐ Anger
☐ Freedom ☐ Paralysis ☐ Confusion ☐ Panic
☐ Joy ☐ Surprise ☐ Vulnerability ☐ ____________

HAVE YOU DREAMED THIS DREAM BEFORE?

☐ Yes ☐ No ☐ Maybe so ☐ I wish ☐ Once was enough, thanks

SKETCH

HOW WOULD YOU DRAW IT?

☐ Frame-worthy ☐ An accurate rendering ☐ Close enough ☐ Crap

REFLECT

WHAT'S YOUR INTERPRETATION?

☐ Significant ☐ Insignificant ☐ Reexamine later ☐ Dream understood

RECORD
WHAT HAPPENED?

TITLE:

DATE:

☐ Nightmare ☐ Fantasy ☐ Symbolic ☐ Mundane ☐ Just plain bizarre

WHAT WAS THE PREVAILING EMOTION?

☐ Fear ☐ Frustration ☐ Loss of self ☐ Arousal
☐ Humiliation ☐ Grief ☐ Love ☐ Anger
☐ Freedom ☐ Paralysis ☐ Confusion ☐ Panic
☐ Joy ☐ Surprise ☐ Vulnerability ☐ ________

HAVE YOU DREAMED THIS DREAM BEFORE?

☐ Yes ☐ No ☐ Maybe so ☐ I wish ☐ Once was enough, thanks

SKETCH
HOW WOULD YOU DRAW IT?

☐ Frame-worthy ☐ An accurate rendering ☐ Close enough ☐ Crap

REFLECT
WHAT'S YOUR INTERPRETATION?

☐ Significant ☐ Insignificant ☐ Reexamine later ☐ Dream understood

RECORD
WHAT HAPPENED?

TITLE:
DATE:

☐ Nightmare ☐ Fantasy ☐ Symbolic ☐ Mundane ☐ Just plain bizarre

WHAT WAS THE PREVAILING EMOTION?

☐ Fear ☐ Frustration ☐ Loss of self ☐ Arousal
☐ Humiliation ☐ Grief ☐ Love ☐ Anger
☐ Freedom ☐ Paralysis ☐ Confusion ☐ Panic
☐ Joy ☐ Surprise ☐ Vulnerability ☐ ____________

HAVE YOU DREAMED THIS DREAM BEFORE?

☐ Yes ☐ No ☐ Maybe so ☐ I wish ☐ Once was enough, thanks

SKETCH

HOW WOULD YOU DRAW IT?

☐ Frame-worthy ☐ An accurate rendering ☐ Close enough ☐ Crap

REFLECT

WHAT'S YOUR INTERPRETATION?

☐ Significant ☐ Insignificant ☐ Reexamine later ☐ Dream understood

RECORD
WHAT HAPPENED?

TITLE:

DATE:

☐ Nightmare ☐ Fantasy ☐ Symbolic ☐ Mundane ☐ Just plain bizarre

WHAT WAS THE PREVAILING EMOTION?

☐ Fear ☐ Frustration ☐ Loss of self ☐ Arousal
☐ Humiliation ☐ Grief ☐ Love ☐ Anger
☐ Freedom ☐ Paralysis ☐ Confusion ☐ Panic
☐ Joy ☐ Surprise ☐ Vulnerability ☐ ____________

HAVE YOU DREAMED THIS DREAM BEFORE?

☐ Yes ☐ No ☐ Maybe so ☐ I wish ☐ Once was enough, thanks

SKETCH

HOW WOULD YOU DRAW IT?

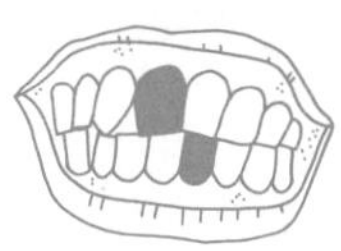

☐ Frame-worthy ☐ An accurate rendering ☐ Close enough ☐ Crap

REFLECT

WHAT'S YOUR INTERPRETATION?

☐ Significant ☐ Insignificant ☐ Reexamine later ☐ Dream understood

RECORD
WHAT HAPPENED?

TITLE:

DATE:

☐ Nightmare ☐ Fantasy ☐ Symbolic ☐ Mundane ☐ Just plain bizarre

WHAT WAS THE PREVAILING EMOTION?

☐ Fear	☐ Frustration	☐ Loss of self	☐ Arousal
☐ Humiliation	☐ Grief	☐ Love	☐ Anger
☐ Freedom	☐ Paralysis	☐ Confusion	☐ Panic
☐ Joy	☐ Surprise	☐ Vulnerability	☐ ____________

HAVE YOU DREAMED THIS DREAM BEFORE?

☐ Yes ☐ No ☐ Maybe so ☐ I wish ☐ Once was enough, thanks

SKETCH

HOW WOULD YOU DRAW IT?

☐ Frame-worthy ☐ An accurate rendering ☐ Close enough ☐ Crap

REFLECT

WHAT'S YOUR INTERPRETATION?

☐ Significant ☐ Insignificant ☐ Reexamine later ☐ Dream understood

RECORD
WHAT HAPPENED?

TITLE:

DATE:

☐ Nightmare ☐ Fantasy ☐ Symbolic ☐ Mundane ☐ Just plain bizarre

WHAT WAS THE PREVAILING EMOTION?

☐ Fear ☐ Frustration ☐ Loss of self ☐ Arousal
☐ Humiliation ☐ Grief ☐ Love ☐ Anger
☐ Freedom ☐ Paralysis ☐ Confusion ☐ Panic
☐ Joy ☐ Surprise ☐ Vulnerability ☐ ____________

HAVE YOU DREAMED THIS DREAM BEFORE?

☐ Yes ☐ No ☐ Maybe so ☐ I wish ☐ Once was enough, thanks

SKETCH
HOW WOULD YOU DRAW IT?

☐ Frame-worthy ☐ An accurate rendering ☐ Close enough ☐ Crap

REFLECT
WHAT'S YOUR INTERPRETATION?

☐ Significant ☐ Insignificant ☐ Reexamine later ☐ Dream understood

RECORD

WHAT HAPPENED?

TITLE:

DATE:

☐ Nightmare ☐ Fantasy ☐ Symbolic ☐ Mundane ☐ Just plain bizarre

WHAT WAS THE PREVAILING EMOTION?

☐ Fear	☐ Frustration	☐ Loss of self	☐ Arousal
☐ Humiliation	☐ Grief	☐ Love	☐ Anger
☐ Freedom	☐ Paralysis	☐ Confusion	☐ Panic
☐ Joy	☐ Surprise	☐ Vulnerability	☐ ________

HAVE YOU DREAMED THIS DREAM BEFORE?

☐ Yes ☐ No ☐ Maybe so ☐ I wish ☐ Once was enough, thanks

SKETCH

HOW WOULD YOU DRAW IT?

☐ Frame-worthy ☐ An accurate rendering ☐ Close enough ☐ Crap

REFLECT

WHAT'S YOUR INTERPRETATION?

☐ Significant ☐ Insignificant ☐ Reexamine later ☐ Dream understood

RECORD
WHAT HAPPENED?

TITLE:

DATE:

☐ Nightmare ☐ Fantasy ☐ Symbolic ☐ Mundane ☐ Just plain bizarre

WHAT WAS THE PREVAILING EMOTION?

☐ Fear ☐ Frustration ☐ Loss of self ☐ Arousal
☐ Humiliation ☐ Grief ☐ Love ☐ Anger
☐ Freedom ☐ Paralysis ☐ Confusion ☐ Panic
☐ Joy ☐ Surprise ☐ Vulnerability ☐ ______

HAVE YOU DREAMED THIS DREAM BEFORE?

☐ Yes ☐ No ☐ Maybe so ☐ I wish ☐ Once was enough, thanks

SKETCH

HOW WOULD YOU DRAW IT?

☐ Frame-worthy ☐ An accurate rendering ☐ Close enough ☐ Crap

REFLECT

WHAT'S YOUR INTERPRETATION?

☐ Significant ☐ Insignificant ☐ Reexamine later ☐ Dream understood

RECORD
WHAT HAPPENED?

TITLE:

DATE:

☐ Nightmare ☐ Fantasy ☐ Symbolic ☐ Mundane ☐ Just plain bizarre

WHAT WAS THE PREVAILING EMOTION?

☐ Fear ☐ Frustration ☐ Loss of self ☐ Arousal
☐ Humiliation ☐ Grief ☐ Love ☐ Anger
☐ Freedom ☐ Paralysis ☐ Confusion ☐ Panic
☐ Joy ☐ Surprise ☐ Vulnerability ☐ ____________

HAVE YOU DREAMED THIS DREAM BEFORE?

☐ Yes ☐ No ☐ Maybe so ☐ I wish ☐ Once was enough, thanks

SKETCH

HOW WOULD YOU DRAW IT?

☐ Frame-worthy ☐ An accurate rendering ☐ Close enough ☐ Crap

REFLECT

WHAT'S YOUR INTERPRETATION?

☐ Significant ☐ Insignificant ☐ Reexamine later ☐ Dream understood

RECORD

WHAT HAPPENED?

TITLE:

DATE:

☐ Nightmare ☐ Fantasy ☐ Symbolic ☐ Mundane ☐ Just plain bizarre

WHAT WAS THE PREVAILING EMOTION?

☐ Fear ☐ Frustration ☐ Loss of self ☐ Arousal
☐ Humiliation ☐ Grief ☐ Love ☐ Anger
☐ Freedom ☐ Paralysis ☐ Confusion ☐ Panic
☐ Joy ☐ Surprise ☐ Vulnerability ☐ ______

HAVE YOU DREAMED THIS DREAM BEFORE?

☐ Yes ☐ No ☐ Maybe so ☐ I wish ☐ Once was enough, thanks

SKETCH

HOW WOULD YOU DRAW IT?

☐ Frame-worthy ☐ An accurate rendering ☐ Close enough ☐ Crap

REFLECT

WHAT'S YOUR INTERPRETATION?

☐ Significant ☐ Insignificant ☐ Reexamine later ☐ Dream understood

RECORD
WHAT HAPPENED?

TITLE:

DATE:

☐ Nightmare ☐ Fantasy ☐ Symbolic ☐ Mundane ☐ Just plain bizarre

WHAT WAS THE PREVAILING EMOTION?

☐ Fear	☐ Frustration	☐ Loss of self	☐ Arousal
☐ Humiliation	☐ Grief	☐ Love	☐ Anger
☐ Freedom	☐ Paralysis	☐ Confusion	☐ Panic
☐ Joy	☐ Surprise	☐ Vulnerability	☐ ________

HAVE YOU DREAMED THIS DREAM BEFORE?

☐ Yes ☐ No ☐ Maybe so ☐ I wish ☐ Once was enough, thanks

SKETCH
HOW WOULD YOU DRAW IT?

☐ Frame-worthy ☐ An accurate rendering ☐ Close enough ☐ Crap

REFLECT
WHAT'S YOUR INTERPRETATION?

☐ Significant ☐ Insignificant ☐ Reexamine later ☐ Dream understood

RECORD
WHAT HAPPENED?

TITLE:

DATE:

☐ Nightmare ☐ Fantasy ☐ Symbolic ☐ Mundane ☐ Just plain bizarre

WHAT WAS THE PREVAILING EMOTION?

☐ Fear ☐ Frustration ☐ Loss of self ☐ Arousal
☐ Humiliation ☐ Grief ☐ Love ☐ Anger
☐ Freedom ☐ Paralysis ☐ Confusion ☐ Panic
☐ Joy ☐ Surprise ☐ Vulnerability ☐ ____________

HAVE YOU DREAMED THIS DREAM BEFORE?

☐ Yes ☐ No ☐ Maybe so ☐ I wish ☐ Once was enough, thanks

SKETCH

HOW WOULD YOU DRAW IT?

☐ Frame-worthy ☐ An accurate rendering ☐ Close enough ☐ Crap

REFLECT

WHAT'S YOUR INTERPRETATION?

☐ Significant ☐ Insignificant ☐ Reexamine later ☐ Dream understood

RECORD

WHAT HAPPENED?

TITLE:

DATE:

☐ Nightmare ☐ Fantasy ☐ Symbolic ☐ Mundane ☐ Just plain bizarre

WHAT WAS THE PREVAILING EMOTION?

☐ Fear ☐ Frustration ☐ Loss of self ☐ Arousal
☐ Humiliation ☐ Grief ☐ Love ☐ Anger
☐ Freedom ☐ Paralysis ☐ Confusion ☐ Panic
☐ Joy ☐ Surprise ☐ Vulnerability ☐ ____________

HAVE YOU DREAMED THIS DREAM BEFORE?

☐ Yes ☐ No ☐ Maybe so ☐ I wish ☐ Once was enough, thanks

SKETCH

HOW WOULD YOU DRAW IT?

☐ Frame-worthy ☐ An accurate rendering ☐ Close enough ☐ Crap

REFLECT

WHAT'S YOUR INTERPRETATION?

☐ Significant ☐ Insignificant ☐ Reexamine later ☐ Dream understood

RECORD

WHAT HAPPENED?

TITLE:

DATE:

☐ Nightmare ☐ Fantasy ☐ Symbolic ☐ Mundane ☐ Just plain bizarre

WHAT WAS THE PREVAILING EMOTION?

☐ Fear ☐ Frustration ☐ Loss of self ☐ Arousal
☐ Humiliation ☐ Grief ☐ Love ☐ Anger
☐ Freedom ☐ Paralysis ☐ Confusion ☐ Panic
☐ Joy ☐ Surprise ☐ Vulnerability ☐ ______________

HAVE YOU DREAMED THIS DREAM BEFORE?

☐ Yes ☐ No ☐ Maybe so ☐ I wish ☐ Once was enough, thanks

SKETCH

HOW WOULD YOU DRAW IT?

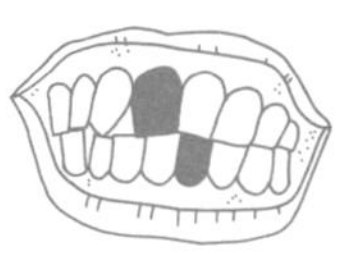

☐ Frame-worthy ☐ An accurate rendering ☐ Close enough ☐ Crap

REFLECT

WHAT'S YOUR INTERPRETATION?

☐ Significant ☐ Insignificant ☐ Reexamine later ☐ Dream understood

RECORD
WHAT HAPPENED?

TITLE:

DATE:

☐ Nightmare ☐ Fantasy ☐ Symbolic ☐ Mundane ☐ Just plain bizarre

WHAT WAS THE PREVAILING EMOTION?

☐ Fear	☐ Frustration	☐ Loss of self	☐ Arousal
☐ Humiliation	☐ Grief	☐ Love	☐ Anger
☐ Freedom	☐ Paralysis	☐ Confusion	☐ Panic
☐ Joy	☐ Surprise	☐ Vulnerability	☐ ________

HAVE YOU DREAMED THIS DREAM BEFORE?

☐ Yes ☐ No ☐ Maybe so ☐ I wish ☐ Once was enough, thanks

SKETCH

HOW WOULD YOU DRAW IT?

☐ Frame-worthy ☐ An accurate rendering ☐ Close enough ☐ Crap

REFLECT

WHAT'S YOUR INTERPRETATION?

☐ Significant ☐ Insignificant ☐ Reexamine later ☐ Dream understood

RECORD
WHAT HAPPENED?

TITLE:
DATE:

☐ Nightmare ☐ Fantasy ☐ Symbolic ☐ Mundane ☐ Just plain bizarre

WHAT WAS THE PREVAILING EMOTION?

☐ Fear ☐ Frustration ☐ Loss of self ☐ Arousal
☐ Humiliation ☐ Grief ☐ Love ☐ Anger
☐ Freedom ☐ Paralysis ☐ Confusion ☐ Panic
☐ Joy ☐ Surprise ☐ Vulnerability ☐ ____________

HAVE YOU DREAMED THIS DREAM BEFORE?

☐ Yes ☐ No ☐ Maybe so ☐ I wish ☐ Once was enough, thanks

SKETCH
HOW WOULD YOU DRAW IT?

☐ Frame-worthy ☐ An accurate rendering ☐ Close enough ☐ Crap

REFLECT
WHAT'S YOUR INTERPRETATION?

☐ Significant ☐ Insignificant ☐ Reexamine later ☐ Dream understood

RECORD
WHAT HAPPENED?

TITLE:
DATE:

☐ Nightmare ☐ Fantasy ☐ Symbolic ☐ Mundane ☐ Just plain bizarre

WHAT WAS THE PREVAILING EMOTION?

☐ Fear	☐ Frustration	☐ Loss of self	☐ Arousal
☐ Humiliation	☐ Grief	☐ Love	☐ Anger
☐ Freedom	☐ Paralysis	☐ Confusion	☐ Panic
☐ Joy	☐ Surprise	☐ Vulnerability	☐ ____________

HAVE YOU DREAMED THIS DREAM BEFORE?

☐ Yes ☐ No ☐ Maybe so ☐ I wish ☐ Once was enough, thanks

SKETCH

HOW WOULD YOU DRAW IT?

☐ Frame-worthy ☐ An accurate rendering ☐ Close enough ☐ Crap

REFLECT

WHAT'S YOUR INTERPRETATION?

☐ Significant ☐ Insignificant ☐ Reexamine later ☐ Dream understood

RECORD
WHAT HAPPENED?

TITLE:

DATE:

☐ Nightmare ☐ Fantasy ☐ Symbolic ☐ Mundane ☐ Just plain bizarre

WHAT WAS THE PREVAILING EMOTION?

☐ Fear	☐ Frustration	☐ Loss of self	☐ Arousal
☐ Humiliation	☐ Grief	☐ Love	☐ Anger
☐ Freedom	☐ Paralysis	☐ Confusion	☐ Panic
☐ Joy	☐ Surprise	☐ Vulnerability	☐ ________

HAVE YOU DREAMED THIS DREAM BEFORE?

☐ Yes ☐ No ☐ Maybe so ☐ I wish ☐ Once was enough, thanks

SKETCH
HOW WOULD YOU DRAW IT?

☐ Frame-worthy ☐ An accurate rendering ☐ Close enough ☐ Crap

REFLECT
WHAT'S YOUR INTERPRETATION?

☐ Significant ☐ Insignificant ☐ Reexamine later ☐ Dream understood

RECORD

WHAT HAPPENED?

TITLE:

DATE:

☐ Nightmare ☐ Fantasy ☐ Symbolic ☐ Mundane ☐ Just plain bizarre

WHAT WAS THE PREVAILING EMOTION?

☐ Fear ☐ Frustration ☐ Loss of self ☐ Arousal
☐ Humiliation ☐ Grief ☐ Love ☐ Anger
☐ Freedom ☐ Paralysis ☐ Confusion ☐ Panic
☐ Joy ☐ Surprise ☐ Vulnerability ☐ ____________

HAVE YOU DREAMED THIS DREAM BEFORE?

☐ Yes ☐ No ☐ Maybe so ☐ I wish ☐ Once was enough, thanks

SKETCH

HOW WOULD YOU DRAW IT?

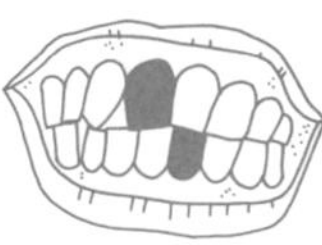

☐ Frame-worthy ☐ An accurate rendering ☐ Close enough ☐ Crap

REFLECT

WHAT'S YOUR INTERPRETATION?

☐ Significant ☐ Insignificant ☐ Reexamine later ☐ Dream understood

RECORD
WHAT HAPPENED?

TITLE:

DATE:

☐ Nightmare ☐ Fantasy ☐ Symbolic ☐ Mundane ☐ Just plain bizarre

WHAT WAS THE PREVAILING EMOTION?

☐ Fear	☐ Frustration	☐ Loss of self	☐ Arousal
☐ Humiliation	☐ Grief	☐ Love	☐ Anger
☐ Freedom	☐ Paralysis	☐ Confusion	☐ Panic
☐ Joy	☐ Surprise	☐ Vulnerability	☐ ________

HAVE YOU DREAMED THIS DREAM BEFORE?

☐ Yes ☐ No ☐ Maybe so ☐ I wish ☐ Once was enough, thanks

SKETCH

HOW WOULD YOU DRAW IT?

☐ Frame-worthy ☐ An accurate rendering ☐ Close enough ☐ Crap

REFLECT

WHAT'S YOUR INTERPRETATION?

☐ Significant ☐ Insignificant ☐ Reexamine later ☐ Dream understood

RECORD

WHAT HAPPENED?

TITLE:

DATE:

☐ Nightmare ☐ Fantasy ☐ Symbolic ☐ Mundane ☐ Just plain bizarre

WHAT WAS THE PREVAILING EMOTION?

☐ Fear ☐ Frustration ☐ Loss of self ☐ Arousal
☐ Humiliation ☐ Grief ☐ Love ☐ Anger
☐ Freedom ☐ Paralysis ☐ Confusion ☐ Panic
☐ Joy ☐ Surprise ☐ Vulnerability ☐ ____________

HAVE YOU DREAMED THIS DREAM BEFORE?

☐ Yes ☐ No ☐ Maybe so ☐ I wish ☐ Once was enough, thanks

SKETCH

HOW WOULD YOU DRAW IT?

☐ Frame-worthy ☐ An accurate rendering ☐ Close enough ☐ Crap

REFLECT

WHAT'S YOUR INTERPRETATION?

☐ Significant ☐ Insignificant ☐ Reexamine later ☐ Dream understood

RECORD
WHAT HAPPENED?

TITLE:

DATE:

☐ Nightmare ☐ Fantasy ☐ Symbolic ☐ Mundane ☐ Just plain bizarre

WHAT WAS THE PREVAILING EMOTION?

☐ Fear ☐ Frustration ☐ Loss of self ☐ Arousal
☐ Humiliation ☐ Grief ☐ Love ☐ Anger
☐ Freedom ☐ Paralysis ☐ Confusion ☐ Panic
☐ Joy ☐ Surprise ☐ Vulnerability ☐ ____________

HAVE YOU DREAMED THIS DREAM BEFORE?

☐ Yes ☐ No ☐ Maybe so ☐ I wish ☐ Once was enough, thanks

SKETCH

HOW WOULD YOU DRAW IT?

☐ Frame-worthy ☐ An accurate rendering ☐ Close enough ☐ Crap

REFLECT

WHAT'S YOUR INTERPRETATION?

☐ Significant ☐ Insignificant ☐ Reexamine later ☐ Dream understood

RECORD

WHAT HAPPENED?

TITLE:

DATE:

☐ Nightmare ☐ Fantasy ☐ Symbolic ☐ Mundane ☐ Just plain bizarre

WHAT WAS THE PREVAILING EMOTION?

☐ Fear ☐ Frustration ☐ Loss of self ☐ Arousal
☐ Humiliation ☐ Grief ☐ Love ☐ Anger
☐ Freedom ☐ Paralysis ☐ Confusion ☐ Panic
☐ Joy ☐ Surprise ☐ Vulnerability ☐ ____________

HAVE YOU DREAMED THIS DREAM BEFORE?

☐ Yes ☐ No ☐ Maybe so ☐ I wish ☐ Once was enough, thanks

SKETCH

HOW WOULD YOU DRAW IT?

☐ Frame-worthy ☐ An accurate rendering ☐ Close enough ☐ Crap

REFLECT

WHAT'S YOUR INTERPRETATION?

☐ Significant ☐ Insignificant ☐ Reexamine later ☐ Dream understood

RECORD
WHAT HAPPENED?

TITLE:
DATE:

☐ Nightmare ☐ Fantasy ☐ Symbolic ☐ Mundane ☐ Just plain bizarre

WHAT WAS THE PREVAILING EMOTION?

☐ Fear	☐ Frustration	☐ Loss of self	☐ Arousal
☐ Humiliation	☐ Grief	☐ Love	☐ Anger
☐ Freedom	☐ Paralysis	☐ Confusion	☐ Panic
☐ Joy	☐ Surprise	☐ Vulnerability	☐ ________

HAVE YOU DREAMED THIS DREAM BEFORE?

☐ Yes ☐ No ☐ Maybe so ☐ I wish ☐ Once was enough, thanks

SKETCH

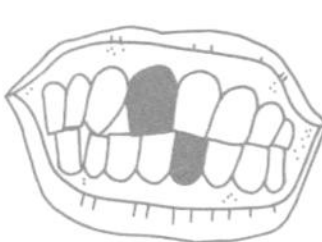

HOW WOULD YOU DRAW IT?

☐ Frame-worthy ☐ An accurate rendering ☐ Close enough ☐ Crap

REFLECT

WHAT'S YOUR INTERPRETATION?

☐ Significant ☐ Insignificant ☐ Reexamine later ☐ Dream understood

RECORD
WHAT HAPPENED?

TITLE:

DATE:

☐ Nightmare ☐ Fantasy ☐ Symbolic ☐ Mundane ☐ Just plain bizarre

WHAT WAS THE PREVAILING EMOTION?

☐ Fear ☐ Frustration ☐ Loss of self ☐ Arousal
☐ Humiliation ☐ Grief ☐ Love ☐ Anger
☐ Freedom ☐ Paralysis ☐ Confusion ☐ Panic
☐ Joy ☐ Surprise ☐ Vulnerability ☐ ____________

HAVE YOU DREAMED THIS DREAM BEFORE?

☐ Yes ☐ No ☐ Maybe so ☐ I wish ☐ Once was enough, thanks

SKETCH

HOW WOULD YOU DRAW IT?

☐ Frame-worthy ☐ An accurate rendering ☐ Close enough ☐ Crap

REFLECT

WHAT'S YOUR INTERPRETATION?

☐ Significant ☐ Insignificant ☐ Reexamine later ☐ Dream understood

RECORD
WHAT HAPPENED?

TITLE:

DATE:

☐ Nightmare ☐ Fantasy ☐ Symbolic ☐ Mundane ☐ Just plain bizarre

WHAT WAS THE PREVAILING EMOTION?

☐ Fear ☐ Frustration ☐ Loss of self ☐ Arousal
☐ Humiliation ☐ Grief ☐ Love ☐ Anger
☐ Freedom ☐ Paralysis ☐ Confusion ☐ Panic
☐ Joy ☐ Surprise ☐ Vulnerability ☐ ____________

HAVE YOU DREAMED THIS DREAM BEFORE?

☐ Yes ☐ No ☐ Maybe so ☐ I wish ☐ Once was enough, thanks

SKETCH

HOW WOULD YOU DRAW IT?

☐ Frame-worthy ☐ An accurate rendering ☐ Close enough ☐ Crap

REFLECT

WHAT'S YOUR INTERPRETATION?

☐ Significant ☐ Insignificant ☐ Reexamine later ☐ Dream understood

RECORD

WHAT HAPPENED?

TITLE:

DATE:

☐ Nightmare ☐ Fantasy ☐ Symbolic ☐ Mundane ☐ Just plain bizarre

WHAT WAS THE PREVAILING EMOTION?

☐ Fear ☐ Frustration ☐ Loss of self ☐ Arousal
☐ Humiliation ☐ Grief ☐ Love ☐ Anger
☐ Freedom ☐ Paralysis ☐ Confusion ☐ Panic
☐ Joy ☐ Surprise ☐ Vulnerability ☐ ______

HAVE YOU DREAMED THIS DREAM BEFORE?

☐ Yes ☐ No ☐ Maybe so ☐ I wish ☐ Once was enough, thanks

SKETCH

HOW WOULD YOU DRAW IT?

☐ Frame-worthy ☐ An accurate rendering ☐ Close enough ☐ Crap

REFLECT

WHAT'S YOUR INTERPRETATION?

☐ Significant ☐ Insignificant ☐ Reexamine later ☐ Dream understood

RECORD
WHAT HAPPENED?

TITLE:

DATE:

☐ Nightmare ☐ Fantasy ☐ Symbolic ☐ Mundane ☐ Just plain bizarre

WHAT WAS THE PREVAILING EMOTION?

☐ Fear ☐ Frustration ☐ Loss of self ☐ Arousal
☐ Humiliation ☐ Grief ☐ Love ☐ Anger
☐ Freedom ☐ Paralysis ☐ Confusion ☐ Panic
☐ Joy ☐ Surprise ☐ Vulnerability ☐ ______________

HAVE YOU DREAMED THIS DREAM BEFORE?

☐ Yes ☐ No ☐ Maybe so ☐ I wish ☐ Once was enough, thanks

SKETCH
HOW WOULD YOU DRAW IT?

☐ Frame-worthy ☐ An accurate rendering ☐ Close enough ☐ Crap

REFLECT
WHAT'S YOUR INTERPRETATION?

☐ Significant ☐ Insignificant ☐ Reexamine later ☐ Dream understood

RECORD
WHAT HAPPENED?

TITLE:
DATE:

☐ Nightmare ☐ Fantasy ☐ Symbolic ☐ Mundane ☐ Just plain bizarre

WHAT WAS THE PREVAILING EMOTION?

☐ Fear ☐ Frustration ☐ Loss of self ☐ Arousal
☐ Humiliation ☐ Grief ☐ Love ☐ Anger
☐ Freedom ☐ Paralysis ☐ Confusion ☐ Panic
☐ Joy ☐ Surprise ☐ Vulnerability ☐ ___________

HAVE YOU DREAMED THIS DREAM BEFORE?

☐ Yes ☐ No ☐ Maybe so ☐ I wish ☐ Once was enough, thanks

SKETCH
HOW WOULD YOU DRAW IT?

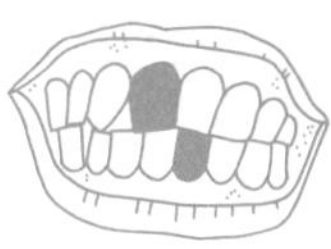

☐ Frame-worthy ☐ An accurate rendering ☐ Close enough ☐ Crap

REFLECT
WHAT'S YOUR INTERPRETATION?

☐ Significant ☐ Insignificant ☐ Reexamine later ☐ Dream understood

RECORD
WHAT HAPPENED?

TITLE:
DATE:

☐ Nightmare ☐ Fantasy ☐ Symbolic ☐ Mundane ☐ Just plain bizarre

WHAT WAS THE PREVAILING EMOTION?

☐ Fear ☐ Frustration ☐ Loss of self ☐ Arousal
☐ Humiliation ☐ Grief ☐ Love ☐ Anger
☐ Freedom ☐ Paralysis ☐ Confusion ☐ Panic
☐ Joy ☐ Surprise ☐ Vulnerability ☐ ____________

HAVE YOU DREAMED THIS DREAM BEFORE?

☐ Yes ☐ No ☐ Maybe so ☐ I wish ☐ Once was enough, thanks

SKETCH
HOW WOULD YOU DRAW IT?

☐ Frame-worthy ☐ An accurate rendering ☐ Close enough ☐ Crap

REFLECT
WHAT'S YOUR INTERPRETATION?

☐ Significant ☐ Insignificant ☐ Reexamine later ☐ Dream understood

RECORD

WHAT HAPPENED?

TITLE:

DATE:

☐ Nightmare ☐ Fantasy ☐ Symbolic ☐ Mundane ☐ Just plain bizarre

WHAT WAS THE PREVAILING EMOTION?

☐ Fear ☐ Frustration ☐ Loss of self ☐ Arousal
☐ Humiliation ☐ Grief ☐ Love ☐ Anger
☐ Freedom ☐ Paralysis ☐ Confusion ☐ Panic
☐ Joy ☐ Surprise ☐ Vulnerability ☐ ________

HAVE YOU DREAMED THIS DREAM BEFORE?

☐ Yes ☐ No ☐ Maybe so ☐ I wish ☐ Once was enough, thanks

SKETCH

HOW WOULD YOU DRAW IT?

- ☐ Frame-worthy
- ☐ An accurate rendering
- ☐ Close enough
- ☐ Crap

REFLECT

WHAT'S YOUR INTERPRETATION?

- ☐ Significant
- ☐ Insignificant
- ☐ Reexamine later
- ☐ Dream understood

RECORD
WHAT HAPPENED?

TITLE:
DATE:

☐ Nightmare ☐ Fantasy ☐ Symbolic ☐ Mundane ☐ Just plain bizarre

WHAT WAS THE PREVAILING EMOTION?

☐ Fear	☐ Frustration	☐ Loss of self	☐ Arousal
☐ Humiliation	☐ Grief	☐ Love	☐ Anger
☐ Freedom	☐ Paralysis	☐ Confusion	☐ Panic
☐ Joy	☐ Surprise	☐ Vulnerability	☐ ________

HAVE YOU DREAMED THIS DREAM BEFORE?

☐ Yes ☐ No ☐ Maybe so ☐ I wish ☐ Once was enough, thanks

SKETCH

HOW WOULD YOU DRAW IT?

☐ Frame-worthy ☐ An accurate rendering ☐ Close enough ☐ Crap

REFLECT

WHAT'S YOUR INTERPRETATION?

☐ Significant ☐ Insignificant ☐ Reexamine later ☐ Dream understood

RECORD

WHAT HAPPENED?

TITLE:

DATE:

☐ Nightmare ☐ Fantasy ☐ Symbolic ☐ Mundane ☐ Just plain bizarre

WHAT WAS THE PREVAILING EMOTION?

☐ Fear ☐ Frustration ☐ Loss of self ☐ Arousal
☐ Humiliation ☐ Grief ☐ Love ☐ Anger
☐ Freedom ☐ Paralysis ☐ Confusion ☐ Panic
☐ Joy ☐ Surprise ☐ Vulnerability ☐ ____________

HAVE YOU DREAMED THIS DREAM BEFORE?

☐ Yes ☐ No ☐ Maybe so ☐ I wish ☐ Once was enough, thanks

SKETCH

HOW WOULD YOU DRAW IT?

☐ Frame-worthy ☐ An accurate rendering ☐ Close enough ☐ Crap

REFLECT

WHAT'S YOUR INTERPRETATION?

☐ Significant ☐ Insignificant ☐ Reexamine later ☐ Dream understood

RECORD
WHAT HAPPENED?

TITLE:

DATE:

☐ Nightmare ☐ Fantasy ☐ Symbolic ☐ Mundane ☐ Just plain bizarre

WHAT WAS THE PREVAILING EMOTION?

☐ Fear ☐ Frustration ☐ Loss of self ☐ Arousal
☐ Humiliation ☐ Grief ☐ Love ☐ Anger
☐ Freedom ☐ Paralysis ☐ Confusion ☐ Panic
☐ Joy ☐ Surprise ☐ Vulnerability ☐ ________

HAVE YOU DREAMED THIS DREAM BEFORE?

☐ Yes ☐ No ☐ Maybe so ☐ I wish ☐ Once was enough, thanks

SKETCH

HOW WOULD YOU DRAW IT?

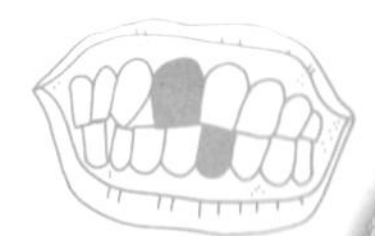

☐ Frame-worthy ☐ An accurate rendering ☐ Close enough ☐ Cra

REFLECT

WHAT'S YOUR INTERPRETATION?

☐ Significant ☐ Insignificant ☐ Reexamine later ☐ Dream understood

RECORD

WHAT HAPPENED?

TITLE:

DATE:

☐ Nightmare ☐ Fantasy ☐ Symbolic ☐ Mundane ☐ Just plain bizarre

WHAT WAS THE PREVAILING EMOTION?

☐ Fear ☐ Frustration ☐ Loss of self ☐ Arousal
☐ Humiliation ☐ Grief ☐ Love ☐ Anger
☐ Freedom ☐ Paralysis ☐ Confusion ☐ Panic
☐ Joy ☐ Surprise ☐ Vulnerability ☐ ____________

HAVE YOU DREAMED THIS DREAM BEFORE?

☐ Yes ☐ No ☐ Maybe so ☐ I wish ☐ Once was enough, thanks

SKETCH

HOW WOULD YOU DRAW IT?

☐ Frame-worthy ☐ An accurate rendering ☐ Close enough ☐ Crap

REFLECT

WHAT'S YOUR INTERPRETATION?

☐ Significant ☐ Insignificant ☐ Reexamine later ☐ Dream understood

RECORD
WHAT HAPPENED?

TITLE:

DATE:

☐ Nightmare ☐ Fantasy ☐ Symbolic ☐ Mundane ☐ Just plain bizarre

WHAT WAS THE PREVAILING EMOTION?

☐ Fear	☐ Frustration	☐ Loss of self	☐ Arousal
☐ Humiliation	☐ Grief	☐ Love	☐ Anger
☐ Freedom	☐ Paralysis	☐ Confusion	☐ Panic
☐ Joy	☐ Surprise	☐ Vulnerability	☐ ________

HAVE YOU DREAMED THIS DREAM BEFORE?

☐ Yes ☐ No ☐ Maybe so ☐ I wish ☐ Once was enough, thanks

SKETCH

HOW WOULD YOU DRAW IT?

☐ Frame-worthy ☐ An accurate rendering ☐ Close enough ☐ Crap

REFLECT

WHAT'S YOUR INTERPRETATION?

☐ Significant ☐ Insignificant ☐ Reexamine later ☐ Dream understood

RECORD

WHAT HAPPENED?

TITLE:

DATE:

☐ Nightmare ☐ Fantasy ☐ Symbolic ☐ Mundane ☐ Just plain bizarre

WHAT WAS THE PREVAILING EMOTION?

☐ Fear ☐ Frustration ☐ Loss of self ☐ Arousal
☐ Humiliation ☐ Grief ☐ Love ☐ Anger
☐ Freedom ☐ Paralysis ☐ Confusion ☐ Panic
☐ Joy ☐ Surprise ☐ Vulnerability ☐ ____________

HAVE YOU DREAMED THIS DREAM BEFORE?

☐ Yes ☐ No ☐ Maybe so ☐ I wish ☐ Once was enough, thanks

SKETCH

HOW WOULD YOU DRAW IT?

☐ Frame-worthy ☐ An accurate rendering ☐ Close enough ☐ Crap

REFLECT

WHAT'S YOUR INTERPRETATION?

☐ Significant ☐ Insignificant ☐ Reexamine later ☐ Dream understood

RECORD
WHAT HAPPENED?

TITLE:

DATE:

☐ Nightmare ☐ Fantasy ☐ Symbolic ☐ Mundane ☐ Just plain bizarre

WHAT WAS THE PREVAILING EMOTION?

☐ Fear ☐ Frustration ☐ Loss of self ☐ Arousal
☐ Humiliation ☐ Grief ☐ Love ☐ Anger
☐ Freedom ☐ Paralysis ☐ Confusion ☐ Panic
☐ Joy ☐ Surprise ☐ Vulnerability ☐ ____________

HAVE YOU DREAMED THIS DREAM BEFORE?

☐ Yes ☐ No ☐ Maybe so ☐ I wish ☐ Once was enough, thanks

SKETCH
HOW WOULD YOU DRAW IT?

☐ Frame-worthy ☐ An accurate rendering ☐ Close enough ☐ Crap

REFLECT
WHAT'S YOUR INTERPRETATION?

☐ Significant ☐ Insignificant ☐ Reexamine later ☐ Dream understood

RECORD

WHAT HAPPENED?

TITLE:

DATE:

☐ Nightmare ☐ Fantasy ☐ Symbolic ☐ Mundane ☐ Just plain bizarre

WHAT WAS THE PREVAILING EMOTION?

☐ Fear ☐ Frustration ☐ Loss of self ☐ Arousal
☐ Humiliation ☐ Grief ☐ Love ☐ Anger
☐ Freedom ☐ Paralysis ☐ Confusion ☐ Panic
☐ Joy ☐ Surprise ☐ Vulnerability ☐ ____________

HAVE YOU DREAMED THIS DREAM BEFORE?

☐ Yes ☐ No ☐ Maybe so ☐ I wish ☐ Once was enough, thanks

SKETCH

HOW WOULD YOU DRAW IT?

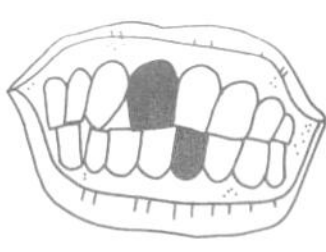

☐ Frame-worthy ☐ An accurate rendering ☐ Close enough ☐ Crap

REFLECT

WHAT'S YOUR INTERPRETATION?

☐ Significant ☐ Insignificant ☐ Reexamine later ☐ Dream understood

RECORD
WHAT HAPPENED?

TITLE:

DATE:

☐ Nightmare ☐ Fantasy ☐ Symbolic ☐ Mundane ☐ Just plain bizarre

WHAT WAS THE PREVAILING EMOTION?

☐ Fear	☐ Frustration	☐ Loss of self	☐ Arousal
☐ Humiliation	☐ Grief	☐ Love	☐ Anger
☐ Freedom	☐ Paralysis	☐ Confusion	☐ Panic
☐ Joy	☐ Surprise	☐ Vulnerability	☐ ________

HAVE YOU DREAMED THIS DREAM BEFORE?

☐ Yes ☐ No ☐ Maybe so ☐ I wish ☐ Once was enough, thanks

SKETCH

HOW WOULD YOU DRAW IT?

☐ Frame-worthy ☐ An accurate rendering ☐ Close enough ☐ Crap

REFLECT

WHAT'S YOUR INTERPRETATION?

☐ Significant ☐ Insignificant ☐ Reexamine later ☐ Dream understood

RECORD

WHAT HAPPENED?

TITLE:

DATE:

- ☐ Nightmare ☐ Fantasy ☐ Symbolic ☐ Mundane ☐ Just plain bizarre

WHAT WAS THE PREVAILING EMOTION?

☐ Fear	☐ Frustration	☐ Loss of self	☐ Arousal
☐ Humiliation	☐ Grief	☐ Love	☐ Anger
☐ Freedom	☐ Paralysis	☐ Confusion	☐ Panic
☐ Joy	☐ Surprise	☐ Vulnerability	☐ ________

HAVE YOU DREAMED THIS DREAM BEFORE?

☐ Yes ☐ No ☐ Maybe so ☐ I wish ☐ Once was enough, thanks

SKETCH

HOW WOULD YOU DRAW IT?

☐ Frame-worthy ☐ An accurate rendering ☐ Close enough ☐ Crap

REFLECT

WHAT'S YOUR INTERPRETATION?

☐ Significant ☐ Insignificant ☐ Reexamine later ☐ Dream understood

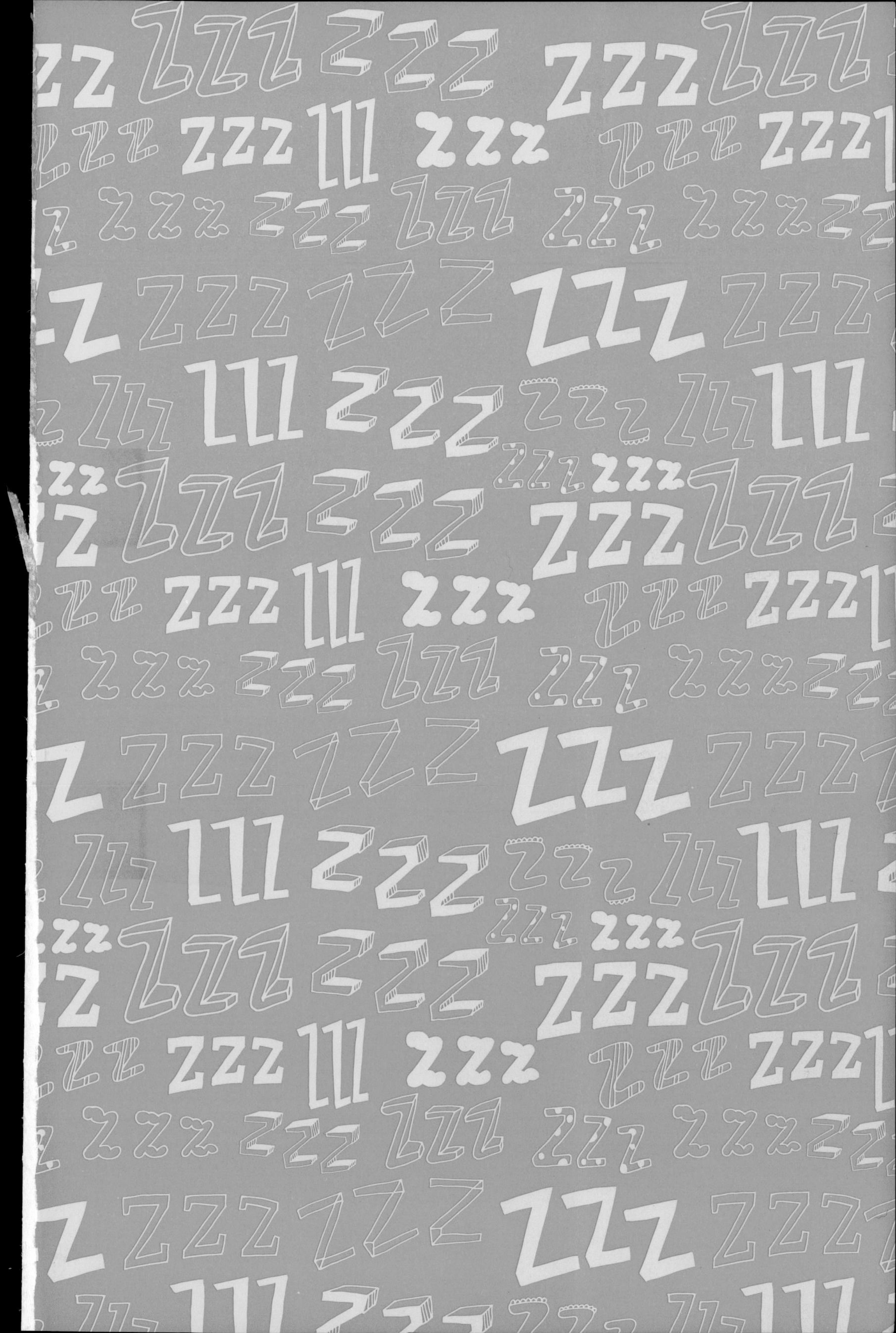

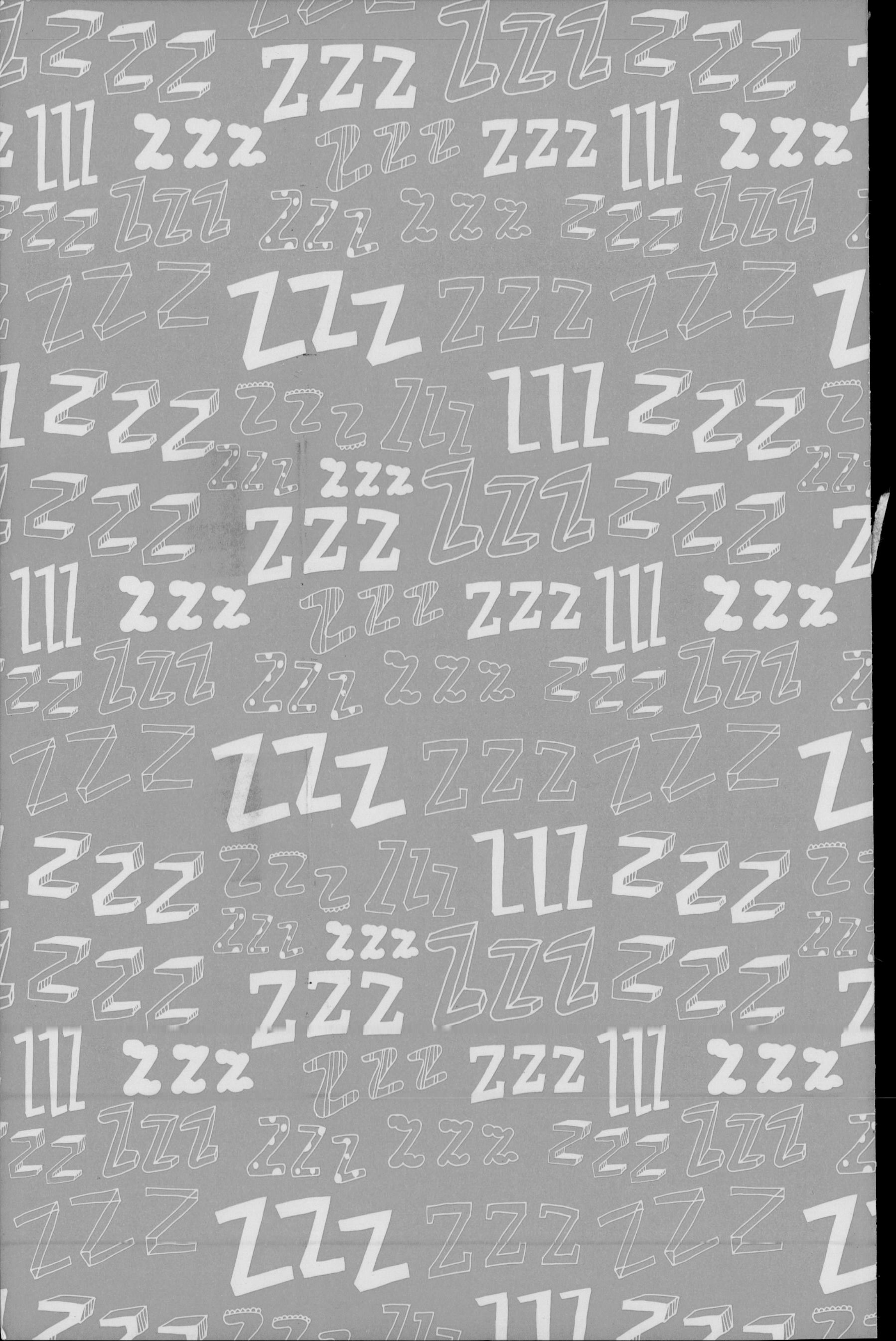